THE
EASY ANTHEM BOOK

THE
EASY ANTHEM BOOK

50 SETTINGS FOR SATB

Kevin
Mayhew

We hope you enjoy *The Easy Anthem Book*.
Further copies are available from your local Kevin Mayhew stockist.

In case of difficulty, or to request a catalogue,
please contact the publisher direct by writing to:

The Sales Department
KEVIN MAYHEW LTD
Buxhall
Stowmarket
Suffolk IP14 3BW

Phone 01449 737978
Fax 01449 737834
E-mail info@kevinmayhewltd.com

First published in Great Britain in 2002 by Kevin Mayhew Ltd.

© Copyright 2002 Kevin Mayhew Ltd.

ISBN 1 84003 882 9
ISMN M 57024 012 8
Catalogue No: 1450243

0 1 2 3 4 5 6 7 8 9

Cover design by Angela Selfe

Printed and bound in Great Britain

Contents

Index of Uses

IF YE LOVE ME, KEEP MY COMMANDMENTS

Text: John 14:15-17
Music: Thomas Tallis (c.1505-1585)

*_'spirit' should be pronounced 'sprit'_

AT THIS TABLE

Text: Martin E. Leckebusch
Music: Stanley Vann

Bread and wine are set be - fore us; as we eat, we look a - head:

we shall dine with Christ in hea - ven where the King - dom feast is spread.

Nou - rished by the bread of hea - ven, faith and strength and cou - rage grow —

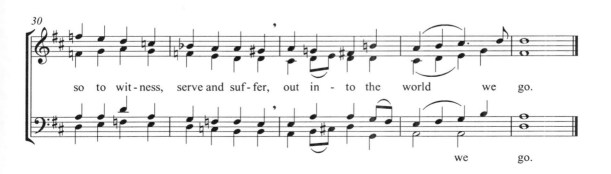

so to wit - ness, serve and suf - fer, out in - to the world we go.

we go.

YOU SHALL GO OUT WITH JOY

THE TREES OF THE FIELD

Stuart Dauermann and Steffi Geiser Rubin,
arr. Christopher Tambling

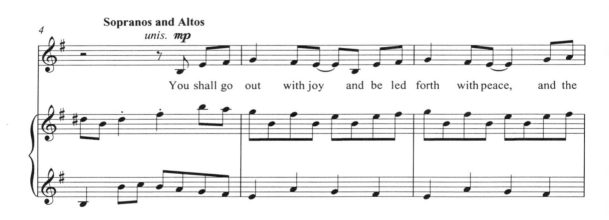

You shall go out with joy and be led forth with peace, and the

moun-tains and the hills shall break forth be - fore you. There'll be shouts of joy and the

trees of the field shall clap, shall clap their hands. And the trees of the field shall clap their hands, and the trees of the field shall clap their hands, and the trees of the field shall clap their hands, and you'll go out with joy.

Tenors and Basses *mf* unis.

You shall go

clap their hands, and the trees of the field shall clap their hands, and the

trees of the field shall clap their hands, and you'll go out with joy.

TANTUM ERGO

Text: Thomas Aquinas
Music: David Terry

o, pro - ce - den - ti ab u - tro - que com - par sit lau - da - ti - o. A - men, a - men.

Translation: *Such a great Sacrament; let us revere with heads bent,*
and let the Old Testament give way to the New Observance.
Let faith supply what the senses lack.

To the Father and the Son let there be praise and celebration.
Health, honour and also strength be given, as well as blessing.
To the One who proceeds from them both let equal praise be given.

in memoriam Kathleen Setchell (1919-2000)

GOD BE IN MY HEAD

Text: *Book of Hours*, Sarum (1514)
Music: Martin Setchell

TAKE THIS BREAD

Text: based on John 6
Music: Andrew Wright

Take this bread, take this cup, come to me and you will not hun - ger.

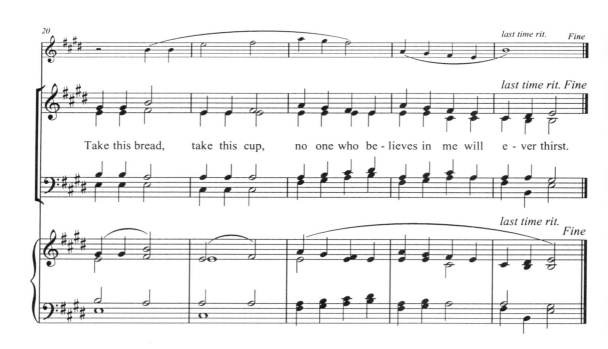

Take this bread, take this cup, no one who be - lieves in me will e - ver thirst.

last time rit. *Fine*

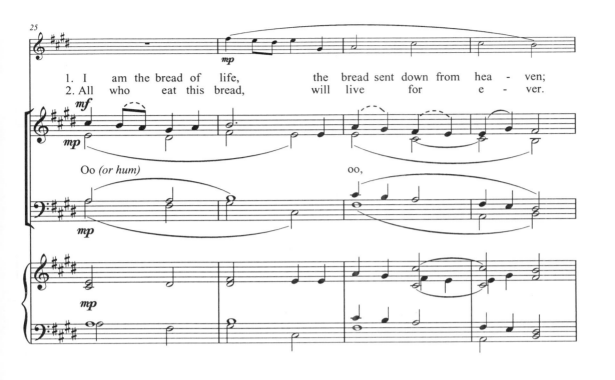

1. I am the bread of life, the bread sent down from hea - ven;
2. All who eat this bread, will live for e - ver.

Oo (or hum) oo,

for the bread of God gives life, gives life to the world.
Eat my flesh and drink my blood, and I will raise you up.

oo.

D.S.

23

THE DAY OF RESURRECTION!

Text: St John of Damascus, trans. John Mason Neale
Music: Robert Jones

day of re - sur - rec - tion! Earth, tell it out a - broad; the
let the heav'ns be joy - ful, and earth her song be - gin. The

Sopranos *mf*

2. Our hearts be pure from e - vil, that we may see a - right the Lord in rays e - ter - nal of Re - sur - rec - tion light; and list-'ning to his ac - cents, may hear so calm and plain, his own 'All hail', and hear - ing, may raise the vic - tor strain.

Sw. *mf*

f

D.C. al Fine

A COMMUNION SONG

Text and Music: Andrew Moore

TO THEE, O LORD, I YIELD MY SPIRIT

Text: J Schubring (from the oratorio *St Paul*)
Music: Felix Mendelssohn (1809-1847)

thee in - he - rit, and death be - comes my chief-est gain. In thee I

thee in - he - rit, and death be - comes my chief-est gain. In thee I

thee in - he - rit, and death be - comes my chief-est gain. In thee I

live, in thee I die. Con - tent, for thou art e - ver nigh.

live, in thee I die. Con - tent, for thou art e - ver nigh.

live, in thee I die. Con - tent, for thou art e - ver nigh.

A DEPTH OF SATISFACTION (PSALM 1)

Text: Martin E. Leckebusch
Music: Rosalie Bonighton

JACARANDA 76 76 D

depth of sa - tis - fac - tion: the pro - mise is made
man or wo - man choos - ing to fol - low what is
trust in God will give us a ground - ing firm and

known to all who turn from e - vil and
right will find God's word be - com - ing a
sure; to dis - re - gard his wis - dom would

11

make the Lord their own; who heed no wick - ed
source of pure de - light: here me - di - ta - tion
make us in - se - cure; Lord, let us not be

14

coun - sel, no cy - nic's mock - ing voice; whose way of liv - ing
cau - ses the fin - est fruit to grow as when a tree is
worth - less like chaff that blows a - way— but guide us and pro -

18

To next verse | Last time

sig - nals o - bed - ience as their choice. 2. The
plant - ed where streams of wa - ter flow. 3. To
tect us; watch o - ver us each day.

GOD IS

Text: Brian Foley, based on Psalm 150
Music: John Marsh

life to be and move, with mind to think and un-der-stand, with

mind to think and un-der-stand, with

heart to feel and love. Praise him with ev-'ry-thing we do, with

ev-'ry-thing we make; praise him in things of ev-'ry day made

ho - ly for his sake! Praise him with ev-'ry art and skill, with beau - ty and with

grace; with ev-'ry-thing, in ev-'ry-thing, praise God with ev-'ry praise!

COMFORT, O LORD, THE SOUL OF THY SERVANT

Text: Psalm 86:4
Music: William Crotch (1775-1847)

ser - vant, for un - to thee do I lift up my

soul, do I lift up my soul. Com - fort, O Lord, the

soul of thy ser - vant, for un - to thee do I

lift up my soul, do I lift up my soul.

LIKE THE DEER THAT YEARNS

Text: paraphrase of Psalms (41) 42 and (42) 43, Grail translation
Music: Andrew Moore

The Refrain may begin with any solo voice on a single line for the first time.
Thereafter, it may begin in unison and the melody of the entire Refrain
may be sung by the congregation.

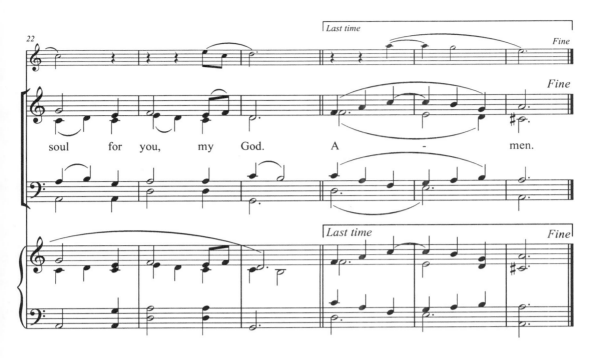

soul for you, my God. A - men.

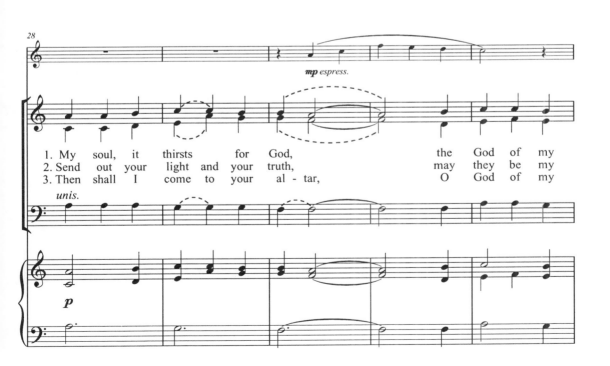

1. My soul, it thirsts for God, the God of my
2. Send out your light and your truth, may they be my
3. Then shall I come to your al - tar, O God of my

unis.

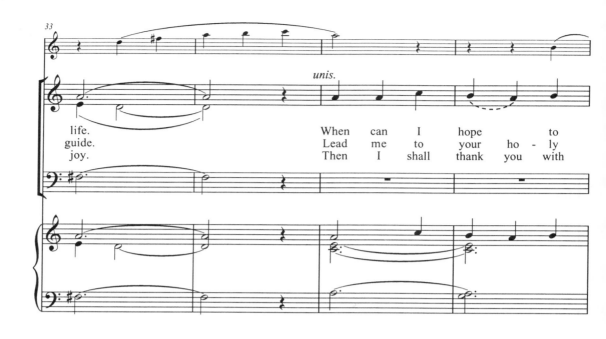

life.   When can I hope to
guide.   Lead me to your ho - ly
joy.   Then I shall thank you with

see   the face, the face of my God.
moun - tain, the place, the place where you are.
mu - sic   O Lord, O Lord my God.

hope to see
ho - ly moun - tain,
thank you with mu - sic

HAIL, TRUE BODY

Text: 14th century Latin, trans. Henry Oxenham (1829-1888) alt.
Music: Michael Higgins

PRAISE WE OUR GOD WITH JOY

Text: Frederick Oakeley
Music: David Terry

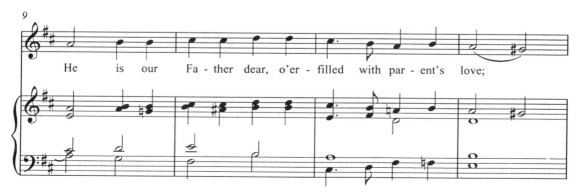

mer - cies un - sought, un - known, he show - ers from a - bove.

He is our Shep - herd true; with

watch - ful care un - sleep - ing, on us, his err - ing sheep, an

eye of pi - ty keep - ing; he with a migh - ty arm the

bonds of sin doth break and to our bur - dened hearts in

words of peace doth speak.

Sopranos

Gra - ces in cop - ious stream from that pure fount are well - ing,

All other voices

where, from our heart of hearts, our God hath set his dwell - ing.

His word our lan - tern is, his peace our com - fort still,

his sweet-ness all our rest, our law, our life, his will.

43

AVE VERUM CORPUS

Text: 14th Century Latin
Music: Robert Lucas de Pearsall (1795-1856)

O cle-mens, O pi - e, O dul - cis Je - su, Je - su, Je - su,

Fi - li Ma - ri - ae, Fi - li Ma - ri - ae.

Translation: Hail true body of the Virgin Mary
which truly suffered and was sacrificed on the cross for the human race,
whose pierced side poured with water and blood:
be to us a foretaste of the verdict to be passed at death.

COME WITH NEWLY-WRITTEN ANTHEMS (PSALM 98)

Text: Martin E. Leckebusch
Music: Stanley Vann

STIBBINGTON 87 87 D

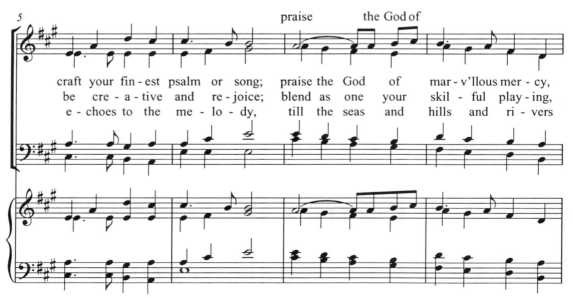

47

WE LIFT OUR HEARTS IN WORSHIP

Text: Martin E. Leckebusch
Music: Colin Mawby

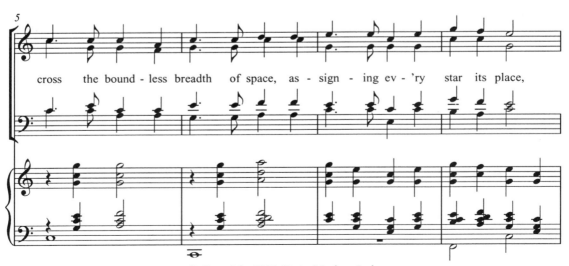

Lord God, your sov-'reign hand we trace, and of - fer you our wor - ship.

Your vast de - sign is

BREAD OF HEAVEN

Text: Josiah Conder (1789-1855)
Music: Robert Jones

COME, PREPARE THE WAY

An Anthem for Advent

Text: Nick Fawcett
Music: Trumpet Voluntary (Jeremiah Clarke)
arranged by Christopher Tambling

Come, pre - pare the way, make straight a path in the wil - der - ness; give

thanks and ce - le - brate, the pro - mised day is near.

Sopranos

Let the des - ert sing, the hills re - joice, tell out his sto - ry,

let the hea - vens ring, the earth in greet - ing call.

Wel - come now the King, lift up your voice, pro - claim his glo - ry,

for he comes to bring new life, new hope to all.

Come, pre - pare the way, make straight a path in the wil - der - ness; give

thanks and ce - le - brate, the pro - mised day is near.

Sound out the trum - pets, sound out the trum - pets, he shall reign for e - ver - more.

Sing out his praise, sing out his prai - ses, wor - ship and a - dore.

Come, pre - pare the way, make straight a path in the wil - der - ness; give

thanks and ce - le - brate, the pro - mised day is near.

JESUS, EVERY THOUGHT AND WORD

Text: Brian Foley
Music: John Marsh

GOD BEYOND EARTH'S FINEST TREASURES (PSALM 16)

Text: Martin E. Leckebusch
Music: Richard Lloyd

WALDEN 87 87 44 7

Unison

1. God be-yond earth's fi-nest trea-sures, you a-lone shall have my praise;
3. When my earth-ly days are o-ver, fresh de-lights re-main in store:

I will love your che-rished peo-ple, I will serve you all my days;
vast-er rich-es, full-er plea-sures than I e-ver knew be-fore—

Fine

be my ru-ler, be my ref-uge, God the guar-dian of my ways.
life un-end-ing, joy un-fad-ing in your pre-sence e-ver-more.

Harmony

2. You have caused my life to pros-per — count-less gifts your love has planned!

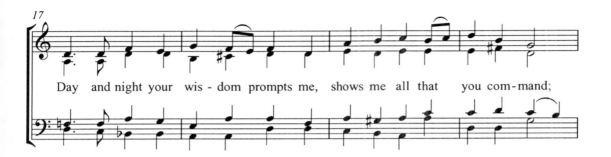

Day and night your wis-dom prompts me, shows me all that you com-mand;

D.C. al Fine

God be-fore me, God be-side me, safe with-in your care I stand.

I WILL SING YOUR MERCIES, LORD (PSALM 30)

Text: Martin E. Leckebusch
Music: Stanley Vann

SWALEDALE 77 77

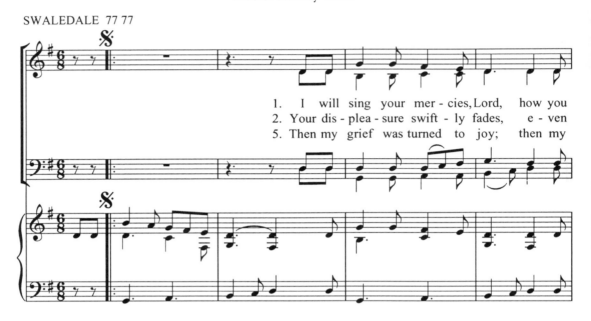

1. I will sing your mer - cies, Lord, how you
2. Your dis - plea - sure swift - ly fades, e - ven
5. Then my grief was turned to joy; then my

heard and ans - wered prayer: foes dis - armed and fears re -
when your an - ger burns; though the night is full of
laugh - ter was re - stored — one un - end - ing song of

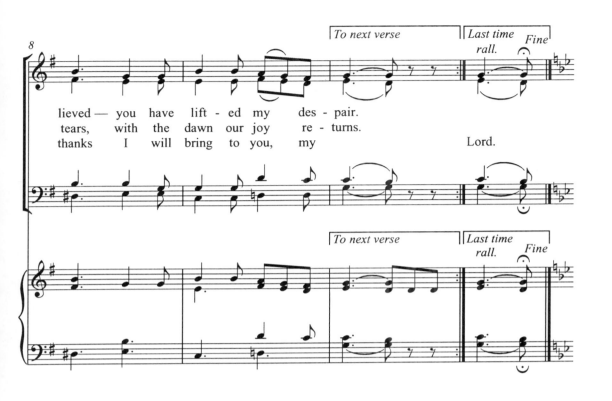

lieved — you have lift - ed my des - pair.
tears, with the dawn our joy re - turns.
thanks I will bring to you, my Lord.

3. I have tast - ed both ex - tremes, con - fi -
4. In pro - found dis - tress I prayed: 'Gra - cious

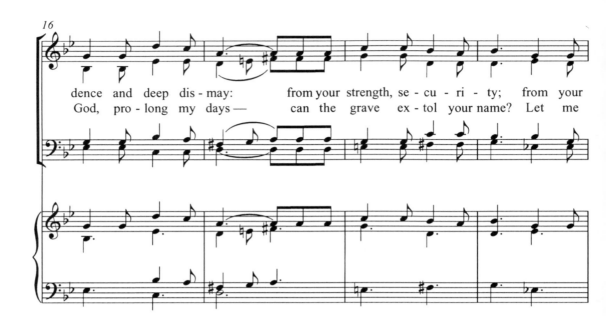

dence and deep dis - may: from your strength, se - cu - ri - ty;   from your
God, pro - long my days —   can the grave ex - tol your name? Let me

si - lence, dis - ar - ray.
live, and sing your   praise!'

LET ALL MORTAL FLESH KEEP SILENCE

Text: Liturgy of St James, trans. G. Moultrie (1829-1885)
Music: David Terry

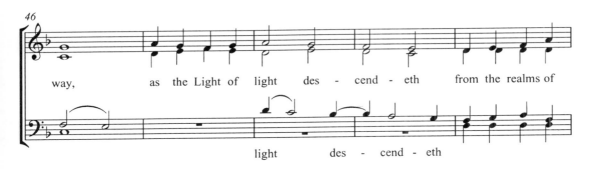

way, as the Light of light des - cend - eth from the realms of

light des - cend - eth

end - less day, that the pow'rs of hell may

that the pow'rs of

dim. molto

van - ish as the dark-ness clears a - way.
a - way.

dim. molto

hell may van - ish as the dark-ness clears a - way.

HAIL, TRUE BODY

Text: 14th century Latin, trans. Henry Oxenham (1829-1888)
Music: Andrew Fletcher

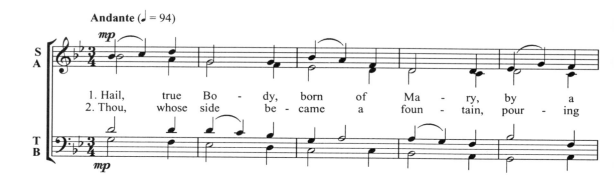

O sweet-est Je - su, O gra-cious Je - su,

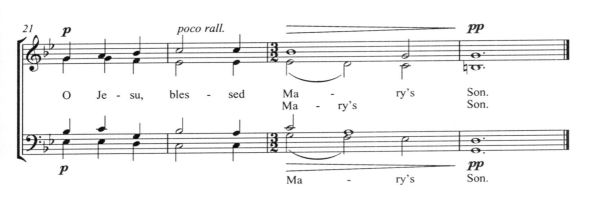

O Je - su, bles - sed Ma - ry's Son.
Ma - ry's Son.

Ma - ry's Son.

THEN LET US GO

Text: Martin E. Leckebusch
Music: John Marsh

WITH GOD MY SAVIOUR AS MY LIGHT (PSALM 27)

Text: Martin E. Leckebusch
Music: Betty Roe

WAVENEY 86 86 (CM)

1. With God my Sa-viour as my Light, why should I be a-fraid? The
3. The fo-cus of my prayer is this: that I may see his face, and
5. So when I find my-self at risk from lurk-ing trea-che-ry, Lord,

fierc-est foes who threat-en me will find me un-dis-mayed. 2. God's
prove his mer-cy more than plumbs the depths of my dis-grace. 4. And
show me how to walk with you in full in-te-gri-ty. 6. For

tem-ple is my cho-sen home; his beau-ty draws my gaze — though
should my ve-ry fa-mi-ly ac-know-ledge me no more, the
this I know: through-out my life your love will hold me fast — and

trou-bles rage on ev-'ry side my heart still flows with praise.
Lord re-mains my hid-ing-place — in him I rest se-cure.
I shall trust and hope in you from this day to my last.

SUCH LOVE

Graham Kendrick, arr. Christopher Tambling

Gently
Soprano Solo *mp*

1. Such love, pure as the whit - est snow; such
love weeps for the shame I know; such love,
pay - ing the debt I owe; O Je - sus, such
love.

Sopranos and Altos
unis. *mp*

2. Such love,
Man.

still - ing my rest - less - ness; such love, fill - ing my

emp - ti - ness; such love, show-ing me ho - li - ness;

O Je - sus, such love.

3. Such love

springs from e - ter - ni - ty; such love, stream-ing through

springs from e - ter - ni - ty;

for C.P.T

AVE VERUM

Text: Innocent VI
Music: David Terry

Translation: Hail, true body born of the Virgin Mary;
truly suffering and sacrificed on the cross for mankind.
You, whose pierced side yielded true blood,
be our food in the trials of death.

COME, PRAISE THE LORD

Text: Martin E. Leckebusch
Music: Brian Glading

wor-ship and a-dore and ex-alt his name — he is wor - thy to be
love for you is great and his faith - ful - ness is un - end - ing — bless the

praised, to be praised, to be praised for e - ver - more.
Lord, bless the Lord, bless the Lord, and ce - le - brate!

NOW LET US FROM THIS TABLE RISE

Text: Fred Kaan
Music: Norman Warren

With minds a-lert, up-held by grace, to spread the word in speech and deed, we

fol-low in the steps of Christ, at one with all in hope and need.

Gt.

Tenors and Basses *mf*

To fill each hu-man house with love, it is the sa-cra-

Ped.

ment of care; the work that Christ be - gan to do we hum-bly pledge our-selves to share.

Then

Man.

mf

Ped.

grant us grace, com - pan - ion God, to choose a - gain the pil - grim way, and

help us to ac - cept with joy the chal - lenge of to -

mor - row's day, the chal - lenge of to - mor - row's

day.

LORD, HEAR THE LONELY SUFFERER'S CRY (PSALM 22)

Text: Martin E. Leckebusch
Music: Colin Mawby

FERNHURST 88 88 87 87

Introduction/Interlude

1. Lord, hear the lone - ly suff - 'rer's cry: 'Why, God, have you for -
2. De - nied the joy of self - res - pect, be - set by those who
3. With strength and cou - rage ebb - ing fast, with fierce op - po - nents
4. Lord, hear the joy - ful suff - 'rer's cry — the cry of faith re -

sak - en me? Why does your si - lence fill my ears though
doubt your care, Lord, who could quell the anx - ious thoughts which
close at hand, with life it - self a - bout to end this
fined and strong from one who tells of ans - wered prayer, in -

I pur-sue you fer-vent-ly? For are you not the
pave the path-ways of des-pair? But still your life-long
suff-'rer prays for grace to stand: 'Come swift-ly, Lord! I
vit-ing all to join the song: so may your wor-ship,

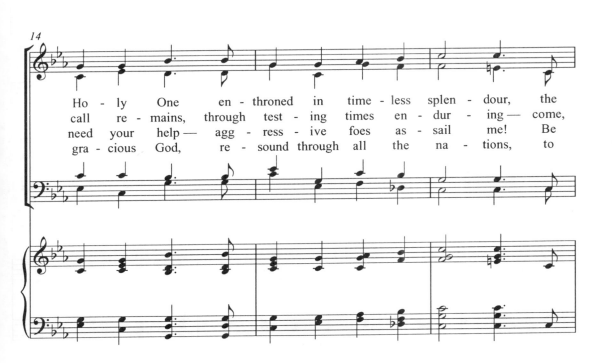

Ho - ly One en-throned in time-less splen-dour, the
call re - mains, through test-ing times en-dur-ing — come,
need your help — agg-ress-ive foes as-sail me! Be
gra-cious God, re - sound through all the na - tions, to

One whose aid our fore - bears knew, their Ref - uge and De -
faith - ful God, your pro - mise prove, the suff - 'rer's hope re -
near - er than the threats I dread — I trust you not to
pub - li - cise your right - eous - ness to fu - ture gen - er -

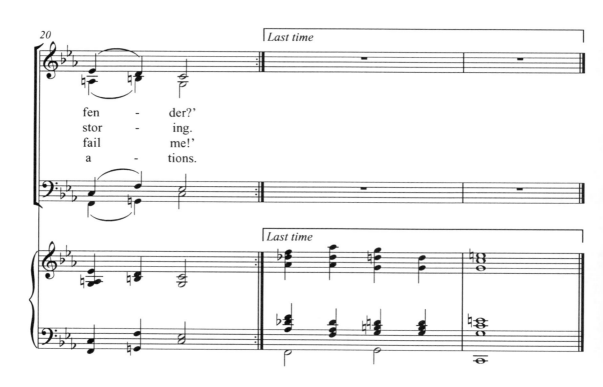

Last time

fen - der?'
stor - ing.
fail me!'
a - tions.

Last time

SING TO THE LORD

Text: Nick Fawcett
Music: Marche Militaire (Franz Schubert)
arranged by Christopher Tambling

Tell of his love and faith-ful-ness, gra-cious-ness, ho-li-ness, let all the world his great name bless, wor-ship now the King! Sing to the Lord, sing a-loud of his glo - ry, lift up your souls, let our

sov-'reign God be a - dored. Tell of his pow'r and right-eous-ness, gen-tle-ness,

stead - fast - ness, let ev - 'ry one his name con - fess, wor - ship now the Lord!

Man.

To the Lord sing praise!

Ped.

O THOU, WHO HAST AT THY COMMAND

Text: J. Cotterill
Music: David Terry

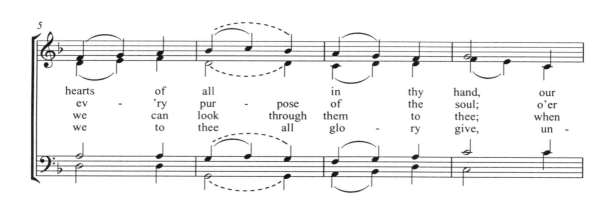

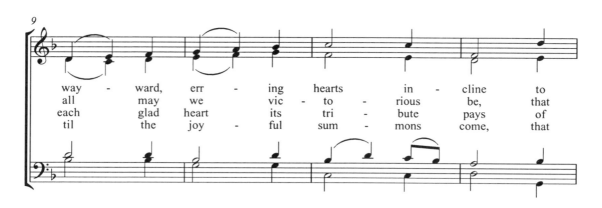

have   no   o - ther   will   but   thine.
stands   bet - ween   our - selves   and   thee.
love   and   gra - ti - tude   and   praise.
calls   thy   will - ing   ser - vants   home.

HE IS EXALTED

Twila Paris, arr. Christopher Tambling

He is the Lord, for - e - ver his truth shall reign. Hea - ven and earth re - joice in his ho - ly name. He is ex - alt - ed, the King is ex - alt - ed on high.

He is ex - alt - ed on high.

ST PATRICK'S PRAYER

Text: Ascribed to St Patrick (373-463)
trans. Cecil Frances Alexander (1818-1895)
Music: June Nixon

Christ in dan - ger, Christ in hearts of all that

Poco meno mosso

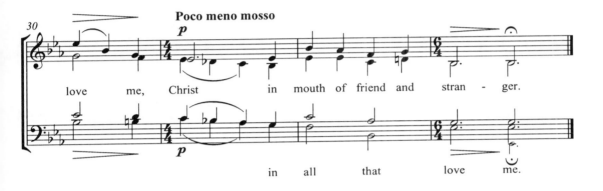

love me, Christ in mouth of friend and stran - ger.

in all that love me.

Respectfully dedicated to Noel Barrington Prowse on his 60th birthday, December 7th 1996

REJOICE IN THE LORD ALWAY

Text: Philippians 4:4-7
Music: Christopher Tambling

101

original words are 'known unto all men'

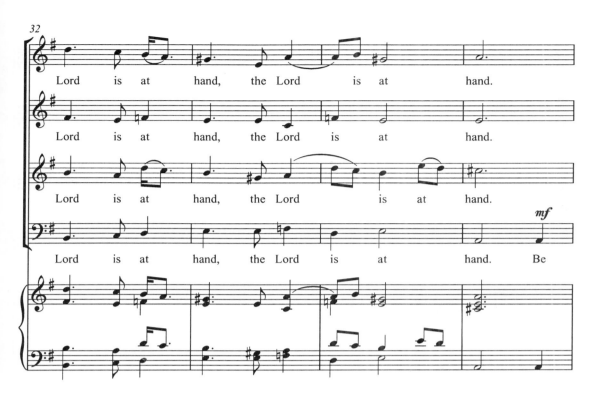

ev-'ry-thing by prayer, by prayer and sup-pli-ca-tion let your re-

quests be known un-to God. And the peace of God, and the

O SALUTARIS HOSTIA

Text: Thomas Aquinas, trans. John Mason Neale
Music: David Terry

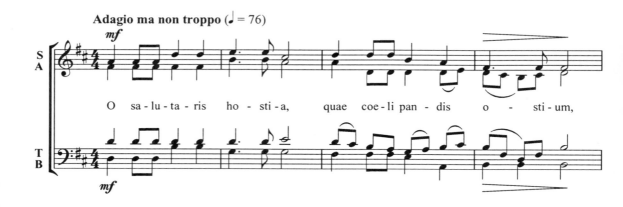

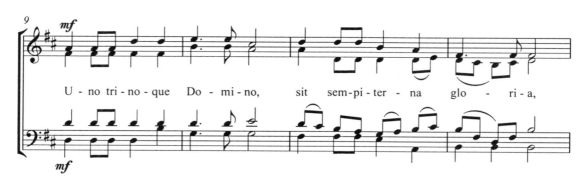

qui vi - tam si - ne ter - mi - no, no - bis do - net in

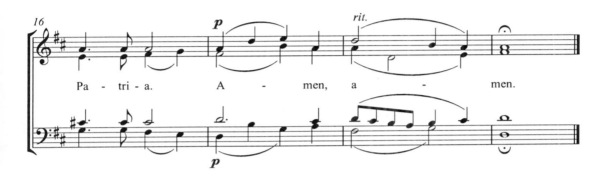

Pa - tri - a. A - men, a - men.

Translation: O saving victim, opening wide
the gate of heaven to all below;
our foes press on from every side;
thine aid supply, thy strength bestow.

To thy great name be endless praise,
immortal Godhead, One in Three;
O grant us endless length of days
in our true native land with thee.

YOU ARE THE BREAD OF LIFE

Text: Martin E. Leckebusch
Music: Andrew Moore

1. You are the Bread of Life which feeds the hun - gry
2. You are the Prince of Peace, the one who of - fers
3. You are the on - ly Way, the Truth whom we be -

soul; your bo - dy, bro - ken on the cross, was
rest for trou - bled, wea - ry, ach - ing hearts by
lieve, and those who place their trust in you e -

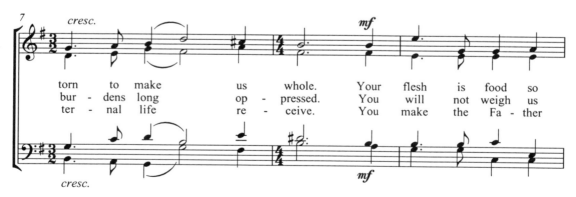

torn to make us whole. Your flesh is food so
bur - dens long op - pressed. You will not weigh us
ter - nal life re - ceive. You make the Fa - ther

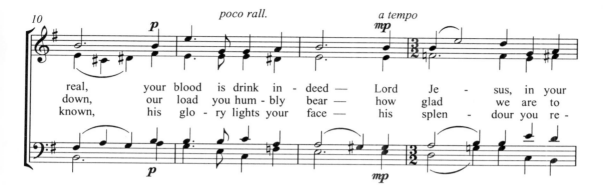

real,   your blood is drink in - deed —   Lord   Je - sus, in your
down,   our load you hum - bly bear —   how   glad   we are to
known,   his glo - ry lights your face —   his splen - dour you re -

life   we find the nou - rish - ment we
learn   your ways, your ea - sy yoke to
veal   to us in mer - cy, truth and

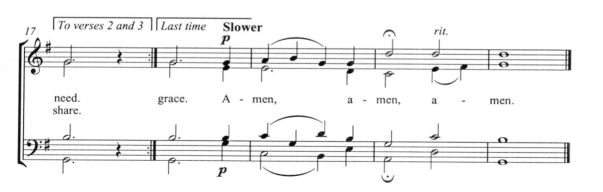

To verses 2 and 3 | Last time   **Slower**   *rit.*

need.   grace. A - men,   a - men, a - men.
share.

109

HAVE MERCY ON ME, LOVING LORD (PSALM 51)

Text: Martin E. Leckebusch
Music: Elizabeth Hill

ST GILBERT 86 86 (CM)

1. Have mer - cy on me,
2. My ma - ny sins I
3. Cre - ate in me a
4. Then I shall tell my

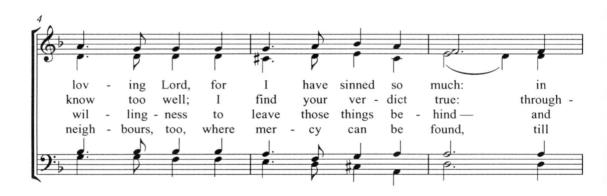

lov - ing Lord, for I have sinned so much: in
know too well; I find your ver - dict true: through -
wil - ling - ness to leave those things be - hind — and
neigh - bours, too, where mer - cy can be found, till

To verses 2, 3, 4

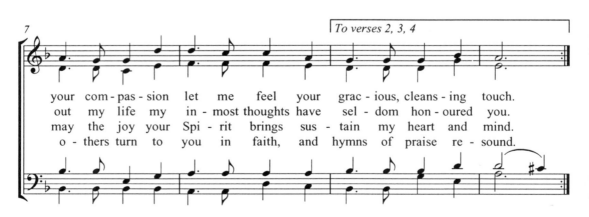

your com - pas - sion let me feel your grac - ious, cleans - ing touch.
out my life my in - most thoughts have sel - dom hon - oured you.
may the joy your Spi - rit brings sus - tain my heart and mind.
o - thers turn to you in faith, and hymns of praise re - sound.

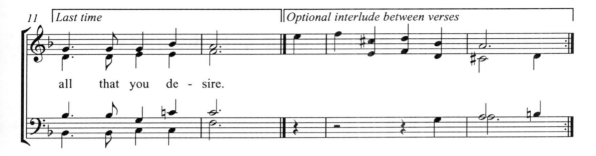

5. For contrite hearts are your delight —
   what more do you require?
   The off'rings born of brokenness
   are all that you desire.

I AM THE LIGHT OF THE WORLD

Text: John 8:12
Music: Rosalie Bonighton

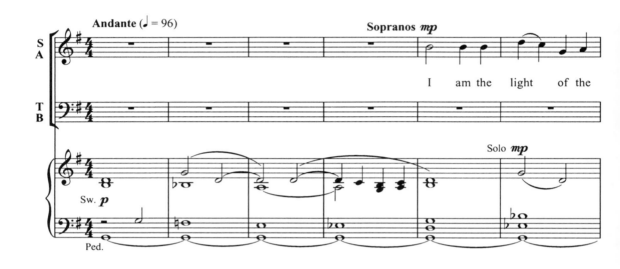

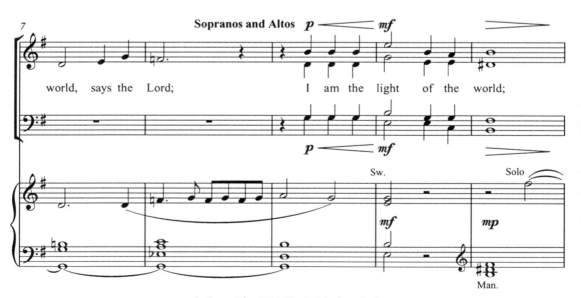

SOUND OUT HIS PRAISES

Text: Nick Fawcett
Music: Hornpipe from the 'Water Music' (George Frideric Handel)
arranged by Christopher Tambling

Sound out his prai - ses! For God has blessed us with love so pre - cious; his love a - maz - es! His hands have shaped the earth, brought life and light to birth, our world, so rich and full, he made it all. Lift up your

He brought our world to birth, great things he's done. Lift up your

voice and praise the Lord! He is our sov-'reign God, the migh-ty

ff He is our sov - 'reign God,

One. Lift up your voice and praise the Lord!

YOUR MAJESTY IS SPLENDID, LORD (PSALM 8)

Text: Martin E. Leckebusch
Music: Andrew Fletcher

BLAKESLEY HALL 88 88 (LM)

To next verse
Last time

verse dis - played.
new sur - prise.
con - stant - ly.
all the earth.

2. To
3. And
4. For
5. A

5. A hallmark and a signature
   throughout the universe displayed —
   your majesty is splendid, Lord,
   surpassing all that you have made!

O PRAISE GOD IN HIS HOLINESS

Text: Psalm 150
Music: David Terry

Praise him in the sound of the trum - pet,

to his ex - cel - lent great-ness.

Praise him in the cym - bals and dan - ces:

praise him up - on the lute and harp.

praise him up - on the strings and pipe: praise him up - on the well-tuned cym - bals:

praise him on the loud cym-bals. Let ev-'ry-thing that has breath:

Full Sw.

poco rit.   a tempo

praise the Lord.

poco rit.   a tempo   poco rit.

ff sempre

PRAYER FOR PEACE

Text: Prayer for Peace
Music: Margaret Rizza

123

MEMORARE

Text: Brian Foley
Music: Stanley Vann

Praise of you is praise of God for all that he has done; praise of you and

prayer through you are praise of Christ your Son! Vir - gin Ma - ry,

we who love you, we who praise your name, pray, and know that

no one e - ver prayed to you in vain, e - ver prayed to you in vain!

125

LORD, I GLADLY TRUST IN YOU (PSALM 25)

Text: Martin E. Leckebusch
Music: June Nixon

MYSIA 77 77 77

1. Lord, I glad - ly trust in you: let me not be
2. In your hands I place my past: all my sins you
3. Teach me what is true and good; let me hear and
4. When my trou - bles mul - ti - ply you a - lone can

put to shame. As I look to - wards your throne
know so well. Your for - give - ness, Lord, I need,
un - der - stand! In the choi - ces I must make
bring me through: so with all your saints I say,

make your gra - cious pro - mise known: God my ref - uge
for my guilt is great in - deed; e - ven great - er
show my heart the way to take, so that I may
'Be my strength and shield to - day.' Since I know you

and my hope, your pro - tec - tive care I claim.
is your love — mer - cy more than I can tell.
al - ways tread on the path which you have planned.
hear my prayer, Lord, I glad - ly trust in you.

ONLY BY GRACE

Gerrit Gustafson, arr. Christopher Tambling

now by your grace we come, now by your grace we come.

Lord, if you mark our trans-gres - sions, who would stand?
(Who would stand?)
(Who would stand, Lord?)

2nd time D.C. al Fine

Thanks to your grace we are cleansed by the blood of the Lamb.
Thanks to your grace we are cleansed by the blood of the Lamb.

GOD IS OUR REFUGE,
GOD IS OUR STRENGTH (PSALM 46)

Text: Martin E. Leckebusch
Music: Michael Higgins

MANOR ROAD 99 99 and Refrain

1. God is our re - fuge, God is our strength — in our dis-
2. There is a ci - ty found - ed by God, filled with his
3. Come, see his works, his mar - vel - lous deeds, bring - ing to

tress his pre - sence is near; so though the earth quake
glo - ry, held in his care; na - tions may fall and
nought the pow'r of the sword. He is ex - alt - ed

un - der our feet, safe is his keep - ing, what shall we fear?
king - doms col - lapse — still it re - mains, that ci - ty we share:
o - ver the earth — hum - bly con - fess that he is the Lord:

Refrain

Con - stant - ly with us, faith - ful and strong — God is our shield, our

hope and our song. Be still and know that he is the

Lord, e - ver re - vered and e - ver a - dored!

WE ADORE THEE

Text: from St Thomas Aquinas (1227-1274)
Music: Robert Jones

Also available from
KEVIN MAYHEW PUBLISHING...

Short Anthems for Small Choirs
SATB

Mixed Voices 1450183   ISMN M 57004 714 7

You'll find these short anthems an ideal choice for smaller choirs with limited resources and rehearsal time.

Most of the 50 pieces are two or three pages long and none is longer than four pages. All are set for mixed voices. They'll provide even the smallest parish choir with the chance to shine! Indexed for the Church year.

50 New Anthems
SATB

Mixed Voices   1450146   ISMN M 57004 596 9

A Kevin Mayhew mega-collection of the very best new choral writing.

These are all settings for mixed voices, well within the capabilities of the average parish choir, and the music is melodic, beautifully written and harmonically pleasing.

15 Hymn Anthems
15 More Hymn Anthems

Two fine collections of our composers' arrangements of many of the most popular hymns. Their treatment has turned these wonderful melodies into beautiful and devotional hymn anthems.

15 Hymn Anthems
SATB

1450225   ISMN M 57004 915 8

Be thou my vision	Andrew Fletcher
Dear Lord and Father of mankind	Rosalie Bonighton
For all thy saints	Rosalie Bonighton
God is working his purpose out	Andrew Moore
God of mercy, God of grace	Andrew Fletcher
Happy are they, they that love God	June Nixon
I need thee every hour	John Marsh
Just a closer walk with thee	Betty Roe
Man of sorrows	Stanley Vann
O for a closer walk with God	Stanley Vann
O Love that wilt not let me go	Robert Jones
O worship the Lord in the beauty of holiness	Michael Higgins
Soul of my Saviour	Elizabeth Hill
The day thou gavest, Lord, is ended	Andrew Wright
The God of Abraham praise	Andrew Wright

15 More Hymn Anthems
SATB

1450235   ISMN M 57004 954 7

Around the throne of God	Richard Lloyd
Christ is made the sure foundation	John Marsh
In full and glad surrender	Andrew Moore
Jesu, lover of my soul	June Nixon
Low in the grave he lay	Rosalie Bonighton
My God, and is thy table spread	Martin Setchell
O praise ye the Lord!	Betty Roe
O worship the King	Robert Jones
Shall we gather at the river?	Elizabeth Hill
Take my life, and let it be	Norman Warren
The Church's one foundation	Norman Warren
The King of love my shepherd is	Betty Roe
To God be the glory!	Stanley Vann
What a friend we have in Jesus	Michael Higgins
When I survey the wondrous cross	Richard Lloyd